TRINITY
COLLEGE LONDON

CW00666292

Handwritten notes:

Initial £31-

Exam week is
w/c 15th July 2013   16th July 2013
                      9:46

From 5/6/13
230 Ashcroft Road
Stopsley
Luton
LU2 9AB

Next lesson: Tues. 11/6 5.00-5.45
           "   18/6 5.00-5.45
(then normal ½ hr.)

Piano
Initial

Pieces & Exercises
for Trinity College London examinations

2012-2014

Published by
Trinity College London

Registered Office:
4th floor, 89 Albert Embankment
London SE1 7TP UK

T +44 (0)20 7820 6100
F +44 (0)20 7820 6161
E music@trinitycollege.co.uk
www.trinitycollege.co.uk

Registered in the UK
Company no. 02683033
Charity no. 1014792

Handwritten: 89% Pass w/ distinction

Sour Lemons!

Dennis Alexander

Moderately fast [♩ = 63–72]

Fine

D.C. al Fine

Little Playmates

Franz Xaver Chwatal
(1808-1879)

For examination purposes, the marcato marking in bars 5 and 13 applies to the left hand only.

Sunshine

(optional duet part)

Josef Gruber

Sunshine

(candidate solo part)

Josef Gruber

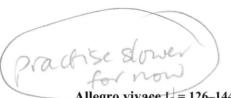

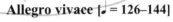

Allegro vivace [♩ = 126–144]

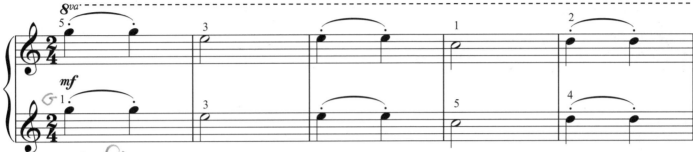

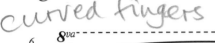

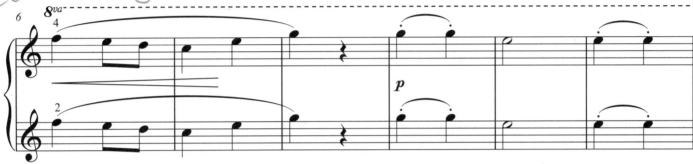

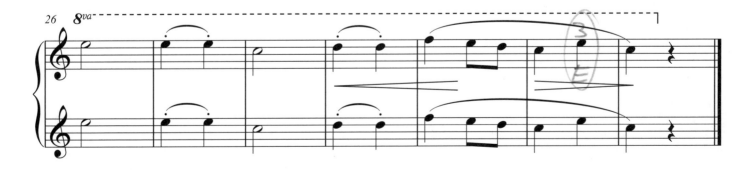

Kindergarten Blues

Uli Gruber

Dynamics added for examination purposes only.
Composer's metronome mark ♩ = *c.* **152**.

The Secret Garden

Pauline Hall

The Little Twins

no. 7 from *Twenty-Four Easy Pieces* op. 39

Dmitri Kabalevsky
(1904-1987)

Alaskan Adventure

Nicholas Keyworth

April Shower

Helen Lockhart

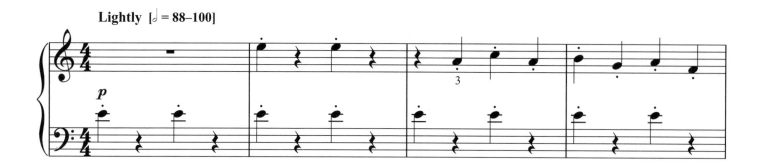

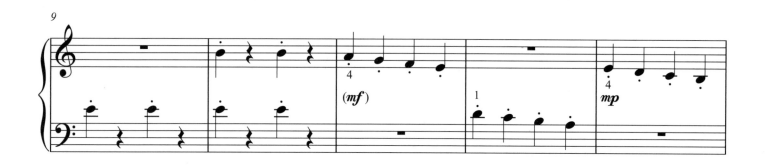

Driving Force

Fiona Macardle

Exercises

1a. First Thing This Morning – tone, balance and voicing

1b. Out in the Sunshine – tone, balance and voicing

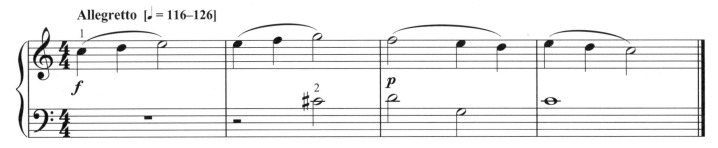

2a. Here and There – co-ordination

2b. Going Out to Play – co-ordination

3a. Super Smooth – finger & wrist strength and flexibility

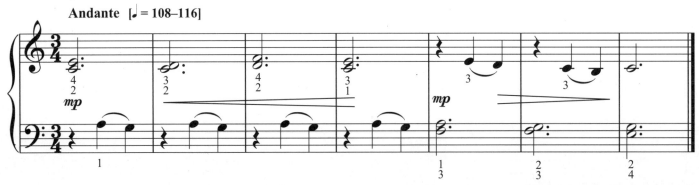